BELLWORK.®

Reading/Language Arts

Level 1

BELLWORK®
Educational Materials

Author
Anne Gall

Contributing Authors:
Michelle N. Barnett
Kent A. De Pue

Editorial Consultants:
Erica Kaiser
Margaret Kinney

Illustrator
José L. de la Rosa

The publisher wishes to thank the following educators who read portions of the series prior to publication for their comments and suggestions.

Rebecca Afghani	Ann DePierro	Lauren Rips
Linda Behrens	Victor Dorff	Ona L. Sandi
Pam Bluestein	Don Felton	Mindi Shapiro
Amy Brophy	Kim Fortune	Lynne Shisbey
Sue Buttera	Robin Harbeck	Ruthie Smith
Mary Johnson Cajiao	Sheri Joseph	Kim Marra Stephenson
Mark Cohen	Rebecca Keene	Kathy Terndrup
Marne Colby	Mia Lewis	Alicia Trent
Erika Daniels	Sarah Milam	Jennifer Williams
Carey Davis	Dennis Regus	

BELLWORK   (800) 782-8869
10529 Dale Street   Fax (714) 995-1181
PO Box 205   www.bellwork.com
Stanton, CA 90680-0205

Printed in the U.S.A.
ISBN 1-932469-21-4

Name Vicolasv.

Fill in the bubble next to the letter your teacher says.

①
- ○ a
- ○ m
- ● g

②
- ○ o
- ● c
- ○ b

③
- ● g
- ○ d
- ○ f

④
- ● w
- ○ v
- ○ y

Name _____

Fill in the bubble next to the letter your teacher says.

1
- ● k
- ○ l
- ○ j

2
- ○ n
- ○ m
- ● w

3
- ● q
- ○ p
- ○ r

4
- ○ t
- ● s
- ○ i

2

Name _____

Fill in the bubble next to the letter your teacher says.

❶
○ m
○ n
◉ w

❷
○ i
◉ j
○ h

❸
○ g
◉ h
○ j

❹
○ e
○ v
◉ y

Name _____

Fill in the bubble next to the letter your teacher says.

1
- ● n
- ○ m
- ○ w

2
- ● b
- ○ d
- ○ c

3
- ● g
- ○ q
- ○ n

4
- ○ q
- ● k
- ○ r

Name _____

Fill in the bubble next to the letter your teacher says.

❶
- ○ b
- ○ d
- ● p

❷
- ○ d
- ○ p
- ● b

❸
- ○ q
- ○ b
- ● d

❹
- ○ p
- ● q
- ○ b

Name _____

For each number below, fill in the bubble next to the correct answer.

1 <u>**b**</u>

    ● is a letter.
    ○ is a word.
    ○ is a sentence.

2 <u>**man**</u>

    ○ is a letter.
    ● is a word.
    ○ is a sentence.

3 <u>**I love you**</u>.

    ○ is a letter.
    ○ is a word.
    ● is a sentence.

4 <u>**G**</u>

    ● is a letter.
    ○ is a word.
    ○ is a sentence.

6

Name _____

In each box, look at the picture. On the line write the letter for the first sound in the name of the picture.

1 b_ed

3 d_og

2 g_oat

4 m_onkey

BELLWORK Reading/Language Arts • Level 1

Name _____

Look at the numbered word. Then choose the word that has the *same sound* as the <u>underlined letter</u>.

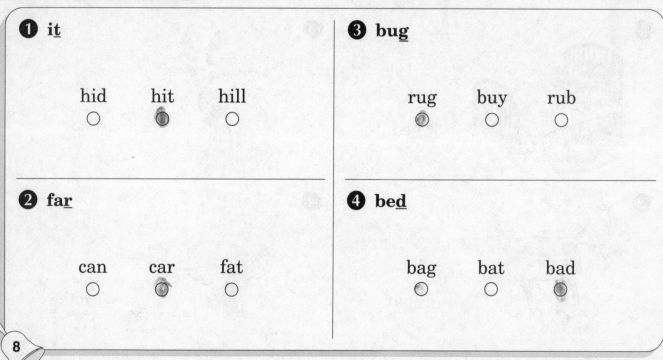

1 i<u>t</u>

    hid   hit   hill
    ○   ●   ○

2 fa<u>r</u>

    can   car   fat
    ○   ●   ○

3 bu<u>g</u>

    rug   buy   rub
    ●   ○   ○

4 be<u>d</u>

    bag   bat   bad
    ●   ○   ●

BELLWORK Reading/Language Arts • Level 1   © BELLWORK Enterprises

Name _____

In each box, look at the picture. On the line write the letter for the first sound in the name of the picture.

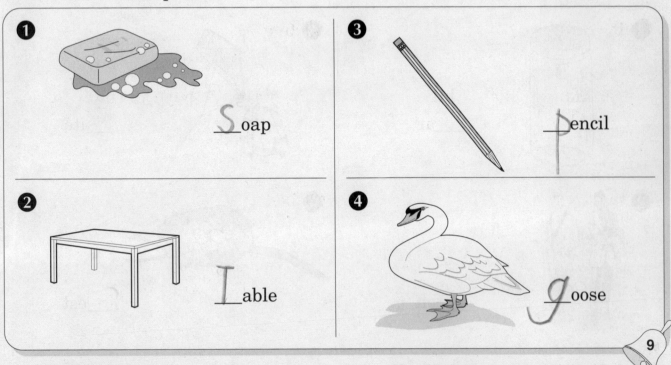

1 $\underline{S}$oap

2 $\underline{T}$able

3 $\underline{P}$encil

4 $\underline{g}$oose

Name _____

In each box, look at the picture. On the line write the letter for the first sound in the name of the picture.

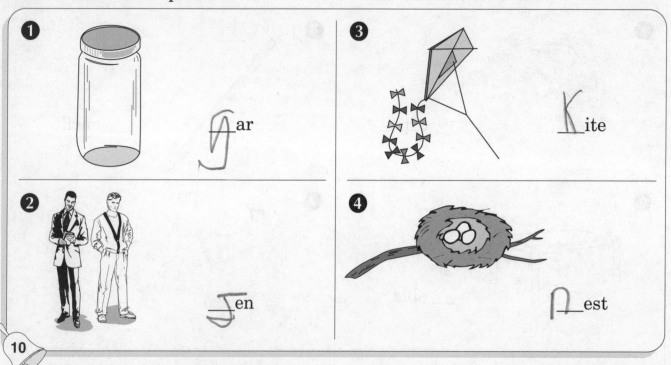

1 _J_ar

2 _M_en

3 _K_ite

4 _N_est

BELLWORK Reading/Language Arts • Level 1   © BELLWORK Enterprises

Name _____

Look at the numbered word. Fill in the bubble next to the word that has the *same sound* as the <u>underlined letter</u>.

❶ <u>fee</u>t

- ○ neat
- ◉ leaf
- ○ bee

❷ <u>s</u>un

- ○ home
- ◉ house
- ○ zoo

❸ <u>b</u>ell

- ○ door
- ○ about
- ○ good

❹ <u>t</u>ime

- ○ letter
- ○ leg
- ○ nine

© BELLWORK Enterprises

Name _____

Listen to the sentence. Then fill in the bubble next to the missing word.

❶ **Jim told his dog to _____ home.**

   ○ go
   ○ Joe

❸ **Give me _____ pencil.**

   ○ the
   ○ them

❷ **We _____ in first grade.**

   ○ far
   ○ are

❹ **She _____ here yesterday.**

   ○ was
   ○ has

Name _____

In each box, look at the picture. On the line write the letter for the first sound in the name of the picture.

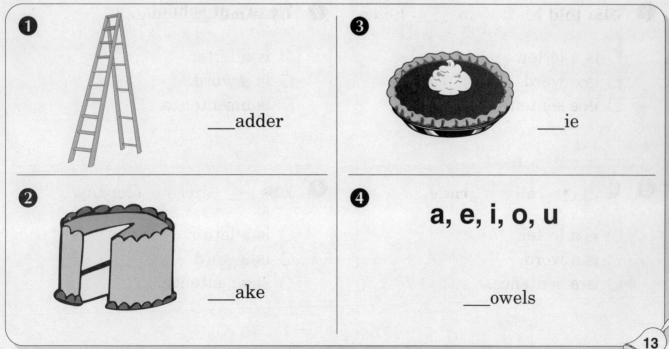

① ___adder

③ ___ie

② ___ake

④ a, e, i, o, u

___owels

Name _____

For each number below, fill in the bubble next to the correct answer.

---

1 <u>cat</u>

○ is a letter.
○ is a word.
○ is a sentence.

---

3 <u>We are at school</u>.

○ is a letter.
○ is a word.
○ is a sentence.

---

2 <u>U</u>

○ is a letter.
○ is a word.
○ is a sentence.

---

4 <u>you</u>

○ is a letter.
○ is a word.
○ is a sentence.

BELLWORK Reading/Language Arts • Level 1   © BELLWORK Enterprises

Name _____

Look at the numbered word. Fill in the bubble next to the word that has the *same sound* as the <u>underlined letter</u>.

❶ <u>b</u>ook

○ do
○ took
○ robin

❷ <u>c</u>atch

○ watch
○ kitty
○ city

❸ <u>g</u>ame

○ wave
○ brave
○ begin

❹ p<u>u</u>t

○ up
○ dumb
○ bun

15

Name _____

In each box, look at the picture. On the line write the letter for the first sound in the name of the picture.

1 ___an

2 ___ug

3 ___ine

4 ___ats

Name Nicolas

In each box, look at the picture. On the line write the letter for the first sound in the name of the picture.

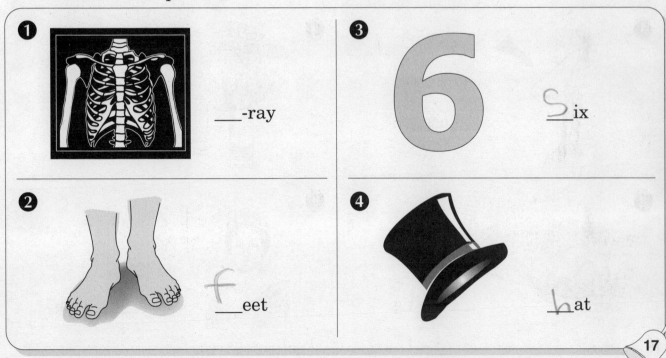

1 ___-ray

2 f_eet

3 S_ix

4 h_at

Name _____

In each box, look at the picture. On the line write the letter or letters for the first sound in the name of the picture.

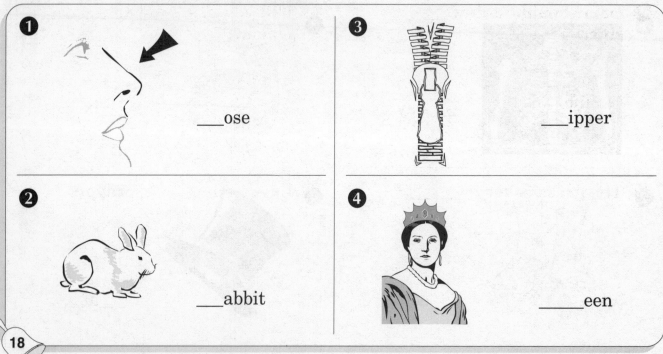

1 ___ose

3 ___ipper

2 ___abbit

4 _____een

Name _____

Listen to the sentence. Then fill in the bubble next to the missing word.

❶ Omar bought a new _____ shirt.

○ boo
○ blue

❸ Will you bring me a _____ lemon?

○ yellow
○ yell

❷ The grass is very _____.

○ grown
○ green

❹ I need one _____ crayon.

○ or
○ orange

BELLWORK Reading/Language Arts • Level 1

Name _____

In each box, look at the picture. On the line write the *two letters* for the first two sounds in the name of the picture.

1 _____ock

3 _____ane

2 _____og

4 _____oom

Name _____

In each box, look at the picture. On the line write the letter or letters for the first sound in the name of the picture.

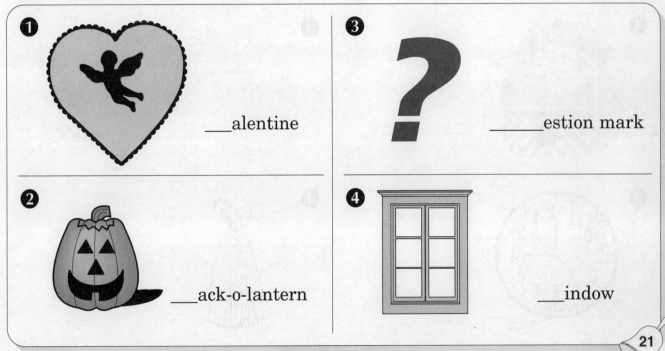

1 ___alentine

3 ___estion mark

2 ___ack-o-lantern

4 ___indow

Name _____

In each box, look at the picture. On the line write the *two letters* for the first two sounds in the name of the picture.

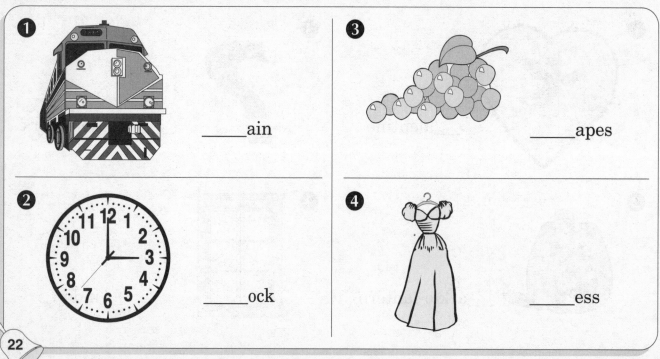

1 _____ain

2 _____ock

3 _____apes

4 _____ess

Name _____

Listen to the sentence. Then fill in the bubble next to the missing word.

❶ One plus two is _____.

○ tree
○ three

❷ _____ shoes make a pair.

○ Two
○ This

❸ I had _____ cookie for lunch.

○ one
○ on

❹ She has _____ fingers on her right hand.

○ give
○ five

Name. _____

In each box, look at the picture. On the line write the letter for the last sound in the name of the picture.

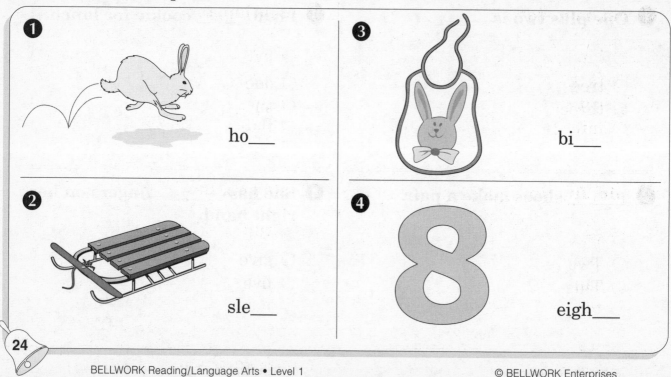

1 ho___

2 sle___

3 bi___

4 eigh___

Name _____

Fill in the bubble next to the word that rhymes with the numbered words.

1 cat, mat, hat, _____

- ○ lap
- ○ tack
- ○ sat
- ○ mit

2 pin, fin, tin, _____

- ○ win
- ○ won
- ○ tan
- ○ ton

3 map, lap, tap, _____

- ○ pat
- ○ mop
- ○ tip
- ○ flap

4 ten, hen, Ben, _____

- ○ Bill
- ○ net
- ○ pot
- ○ men

25

Name _____

Choose the answer that correctly divides the numbered word into its individual sound segments.

❶ mat

○ m/at
○ ma/t
○ m/a/t
○ mat

❷ ten

○ t/e/n
○ ten
○ t/en
○ te/n

❸ husk

○ h/u/s/k
○ hu/sk
○ h/usk
○ hus/k

❹ splat

○ s/pl/at
○ spl/at
○ sp/lat
○ s/p/l/a/t

Name _____

Listen to the sentence. Then fill in the bubble next to the missing word.

❶ Mom wants some plump _____ grapes.

○ purr
○ purple

❷ She bought new _____ shoes for Juan.

○ blown
○ brown

❸ A bright _____ car is coming up the road.

○ ride
○ red

❹ Who gave you this _____ flower?

○ yellow
○ you

Name _____

For each number below, choose the word that correctly completes the sentence.

1 It is <u>fun</u> to _____ in the <u>sun</u>.

    run   bun
    ○   ○

2 The _____ named <u>Dan</u> <u>ran</u> very fast.

    plan   man
    ○   ○

3 The water in the _____ is <u>not</u> <u>hot</u>.

    pot   got
    ○   ○

4 What is the _____ of the boy who <u>came</u> to the <u>game</u>?

    name   lame
    ○   ○

28

Name _____

Listen to the sentence. Then fill in the bubble next to the missing word.

❶ My dad has _____ brothers.

○ sent
○ seven

❷ _____ is less than ten.

○ Nine
○ Night

❸ Put these _____ sticks in a row.

○ mix
○ six

❹ What has _____ legs?

○ at
○ eight

Name _____

In each box, look at the picture. On the line write the letter for the last sound in the name of the picture.

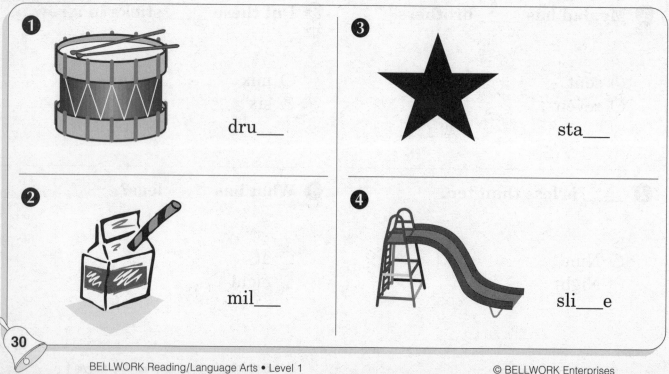

1 dru___

2 mil___

3 sta___

4 sli___e

Name _____

In each box, look at the picture. On the line write the letter for the last sound in the name of the picture.

1   tu___

2   ba___

3   si___

4   ca___

Name _____

For each number below, fill in the bubble next to the word with the *short vowel sound.*

❶
○ at
○ ate

❸
○ road
○ rock

❷
○ team
○ ten

❹
○ mine
○ mix

Name _____

In each box, look at the picture. On the line write the letter for the last sound in the name of the picture.

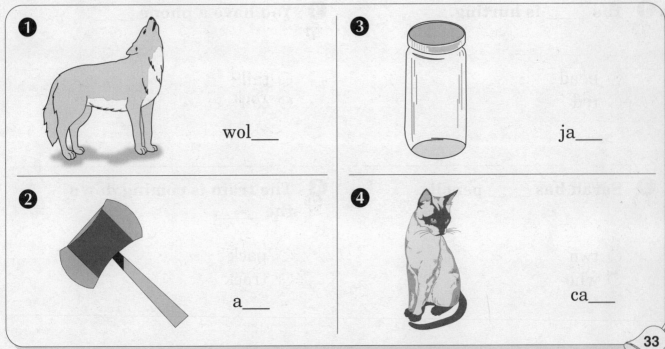

1 wol___

3 ja___

2 a___

4 ca___

Name _____

Listen to the sentence. Then fill in the bubble next to the missing word.

❶ His _____ is hurting.

○ head
○ red

❷ Sarah has _____ pencils.

○ two
○ who

❸ You have a phone _____.

○ tall
○ call

❹ The train is coming down the _____.

○ pack
○ track

Name _____

In each box, look at the picture. On the line write the letter for the last sound in the name of the picture.

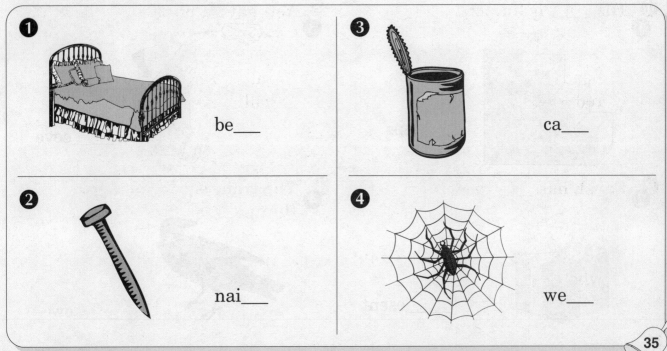

1 be___

3 ca___

2 nai___

4 we___

Name _____

In each box, look at the picture. On the line write the *two letters* for the first two sounds in the name of the picture.

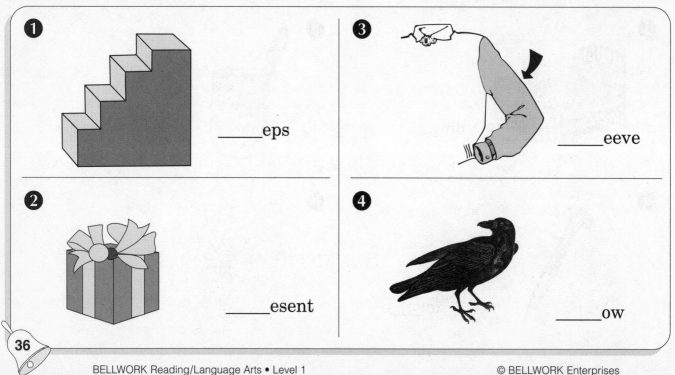

1

_____eps

2

_____esent

3

_____eeve

4

_____ow

Name _____

In each box, look at the picture. On the line write the letter for the last sound in the name of the picture.

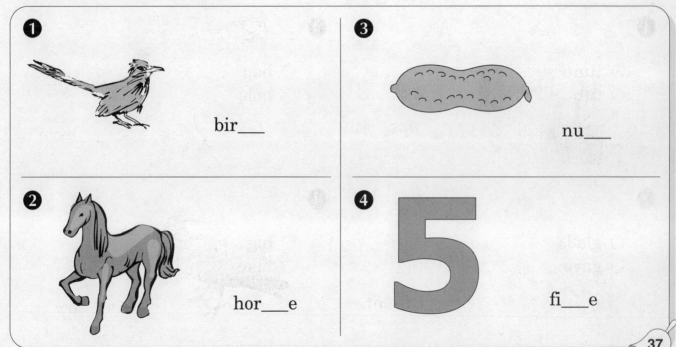

1 bir___

2 hor___e

3 nu___

4 fi___e

Name _____

For each number below, fill in the bubble next to the word with the *short vowel sound*.

1
- ○ tune
- ○ tub

3
- ○ hop
- ○ hole

2
- ○ glad
- ○ gave

4
- ○ big
- ○ bike

Name _____

Read the numbered sentence. In the sentence below it, fill in the bubble under the letter that makes a new word and correctly completes the sentence.

❶ I like to read <u>books</u>.

It ____ooks like rain.

    l   h   c
    ○   ○   ○

❷ We need lots of <u>rest</u>.

I like this book ____est.

    r   b   t
    ○   ○   ○

❸ Where do you <u>live</u>?

Please ____ive me some paper.

    d   g   f
    ○   ○   ○

❹ Do you want to go with <u>me</u>?

____e will go with Mark.

    S   R   W
    ○   ○   ○

39

Name _____

In each box, look at the picture. On the line write the letter for the last sound in the name of the picture.

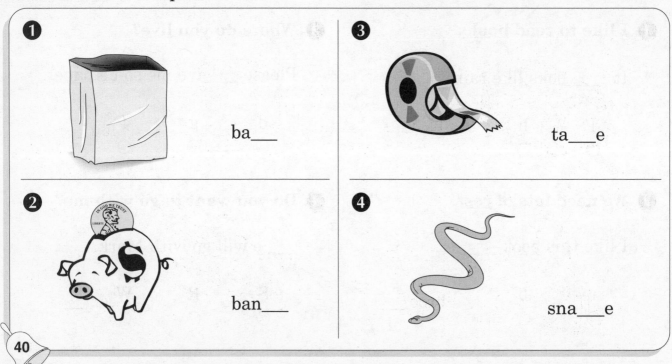

1

ba___

2

ban___

3

ta___e

4

sna___e

Name _____

In each box, look at the picture. On the line write the letter for the last sound in the name of the picture.

1 brea___

2 broo___

3 fou___

4 cor___

Name _____

In each box, look at the picture. On the line write the letter for the last sound in the name of the picture.

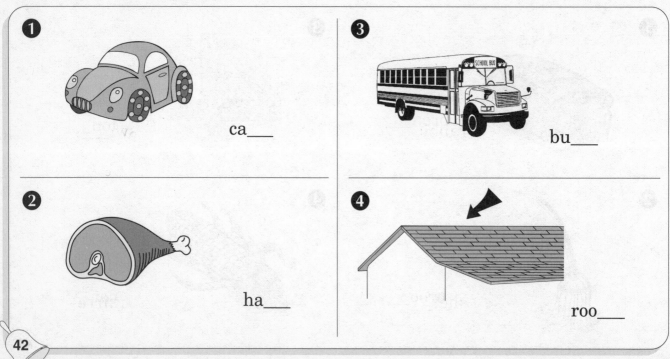

1

ca___

2

ha___

3

bu___

4

roo___

Name _____

In each box, look at the picture. On the line write the letter for the last sound in the name of the picture.

① rabbi____

③ swi____

② shel____

④ squirre____

Name _____

Read the numbered sentence. In the sentence below it, fill in the bubble under the letter that makes a new word and correctly completes the sentence.

❶ I <u>can</u> go to your party.

He ____an fast up the hill.

p ○   r ○   t ○

❷ Amanda got <u>wet</u> in the rain.

Will you ____et me play, too?

g ○   m ○   l ○

❸ Please <u>tell</u> me a story.

He ____ell out of the tree!

f ○   t ○   s ○

❹ Tyler <u>did</u> not like to work hard.

Alex ____id behind the tree.

k ○   d ○   h ○

Name _____

For each number below, fill in the bubble next to the word with the *short vowel sound*.

❶
- ○ mat
- ○ may

❸
- ○ rude
- ○ rub

❷
- ○ hear
- ○ hen

❹
- ○ pine
- ○ pin

Name _____

For each number below, fill in the bubble next to the word that goes with the picture.

1
○ man
○ min

2
○ hat
○ hit

3
○ bad
○ bed

4
○ fox
○ fix

Name _____

Read the numbered sentence. In the sentence below it, fill in the bubble under the letter that makes a new word and correctly completes the sentence.

❶ Take the ball <u>out</u> of the box.

We like ou___ teacher.

t	r	d
○	○	○

❷ The dentist <u>had</u> to pull her tooth.

Marcus ate ha___ and eggs for breakfast.

m	t	s
○	○	○

❸ Did your mom <u>pack</u> your lunch?

She cooked the meat in the pa___.

t	n	m
○	○	○

❹ You can <u>fill</u> the ice cube trays.

These shoes do not fi___!

x	n	t
○	○	○

Name _____

Look at the numbered word. Fill in the bubble next to the word that has the *same vowel sound* as the <u>underlined letter</u>.

1 h<u>i</u>ll

- ○ hall
- ○ hike
- ○ milk

2 m<u>e</u>t

- ○ meat
- ○ neck
- ○ need

3 t<u>o</u>p

- ○ dot
- ○ town
- ○ coat

4 p<u>a</u>n

- ○ pin
- ○ baby
- ○ back

Name _____

In each box, look at the picture. On the line write the letter for the last sound in the name of the picture.

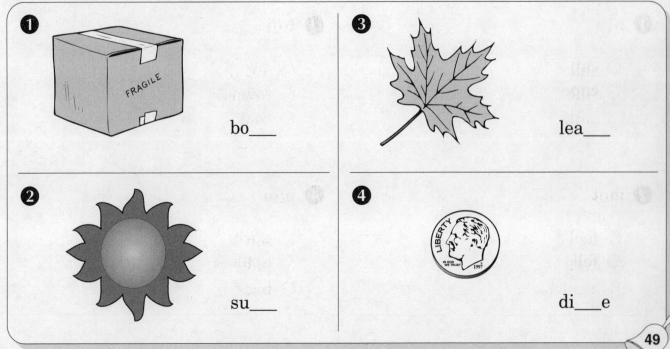

1
bo___

3
lea___

2
su___

4
di___e

Name _____

For each number below, fill in the bubble next to the word with the *short vowel sound*.

1
- ○ cap
- ○ cape

3
- ○ use
- ○ us

2
- ○ feel
- ○ fell

4
- ○ sock
- ○ soak

Name _____

Read the numbered sentence. Choose the word that has the *same vowel sound* as the <u>underlined words</u> in that sentence.

1 The <u>cat</u> <u>sat</u> on the _____.

- ○ mate
- ○ mat
- ○ met

2 Please <u>let</u> me _____ some food for my <u>pet</u>.

- ○ get
- ○ great
- ○ gate

3 <u>Bill</u> _____ go up the <u>hill</u>.

- ○ while
- ○ wall
- ○ will

4 She _____ a <u>lot</u> of beans from the <u>pot</u>.

- ○ cone
- ○ got
- ○ goat

Name _____

For each number below, fill in the bubble next to the word with the *short vowel sound*.

1
- ○ land
- ○ lane

3
- ○ rule
- ○ rug

2
- ○ feed
- ○ fed

4
- ○ fill
- ○ fine

Name _____

Read each group of words. Then fill in the bubble next to the word that *does not* belong.

1
- ○ apple
- ○ grape
- ○ red
- ○ banana

2
- ○ horse
- ○ cow
- ○ fish
- ○ sheep

3
- ○ milk
- ○ bread
- ○ lemonade
- ○ juice

4
- ○ square
- ○ flat
- ○ circle
- ○ triangle

Name _____

Read each numbered sentence. Fill in the bubble next to the correct spelling of the missing word.

❶ The bird is _____ the cage.

○ an
○ in

❷ Adam _____ his dog are coming now.

○ and
○ end

❸ Will you _____ with me?

○ come
○ cone

❹ There are _____ cats at Li's house.

○ two
○ to

Name _____

Look at the numbered picture. Fill in the bubble next to the word that goes with the picture.

1
- ○ will
- ○ wheel
- ○ well

2
- ○ three
- ○ tee
- ○ tree

3
- ○ stool
- ○ shell
- ○ snail

4 13
- ○ teen
- ○ ten
- ○ thirteen

Name _____

Look at each numbered word. Fill in the bubble next to the word that has the *same vowel sound* as the <u>underlined letter</u>.

❶ c<u>a</u>t

- ○ rate
- ○ rag
- ○ coin

❷ g<u>e</u>t

- ○ men
- ○ got
- ○ bat

❸ s<u>i</u>t

- ○ sat
- ○ pin
- ○ eight

❹ <u>u</u>s

- ○ use
- ○ wood
- ○ duck

Name _____

For each number below, fill in the bubble next to the word that goes with the picture.

1
○ want
○ wash
○ watch

3
○ belly
○ bet
○ bench

2

$$3+4=7$$
$$6-4=2$$
$$5-4=1$$
$$2+4=6$$

○ mat
○ match
○ math

4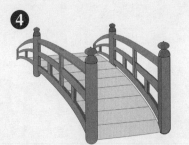
○ bridge
○ bring
○ bride

57

Name _____

For each number below, fill in the bubble next to the word with the *short vowel sound*.

1

○ got
○ goat

2

○ duke
○ duck

3

○ tea
○ tell

4

○ rip
○ ripe

Name _____

For each number below, fill in the bubble next to the word that goes with the picture.

1.
○ Kate
○ kite

2.
○ rain
○ rind

3.
○ bay
○ bee

4.
○ boat
○ beat

Name _____

For each number below, fill in the bubble next to the word with the *short vowel sound*.

1
- ○ rod
- ○ rode

2
- ○ huge
- ○ hug

3
- ○ see
- ○ sell

4
- ○ will
- ○ wide

Name _____

For each number below, fill in the bubble next to the word that goes with the picture.

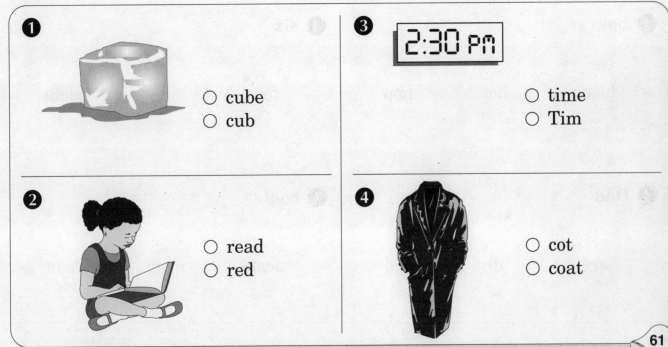

1
- ○ cube
- ○ cub

2
- ○ read
- ○ red

3
- ○ time
- ○ Tim

4
- ○ cot
- ○ coat

Name _____

Look at the numbered word. Below it, find the word that has the *same sound* as the <u>underlined letter or letters</u>.

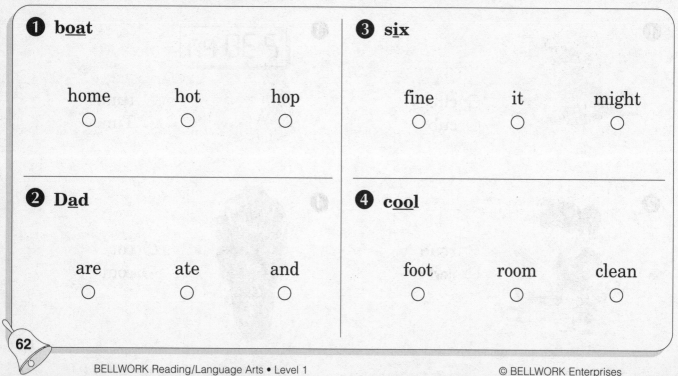

1 b<u>oa</u>t

home ○   hot ○   hop ○

2 D<u>a</u>d

are ○   ate ○   and ○

3 s<u>i</u>x

fine ○   it ○   might ○

4 c<u>oo</u>l

foot ○   room ○   clean ○

62

Name _____

For each number below, look at the picture. Then fill in the bubble next to the word that means *only one*.

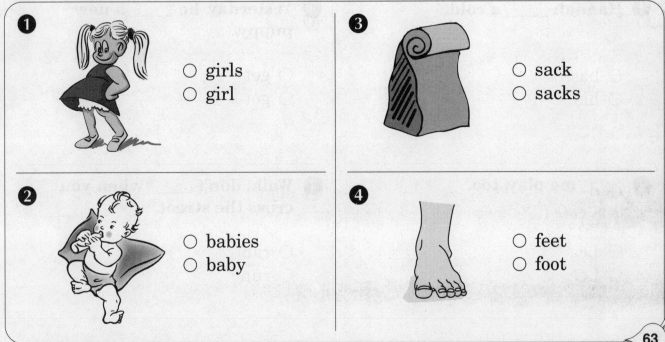

1
- ○ girls
- ○ girl

2
- ○ babies
- ○ baby

3
- ○ sack
- ○ sacks

4
- ○ feet
- ○ foot

Name _____

Listen to the sentence. Then fill in the bubble next to the missing word.

❶ Hannah _____ a cold.

○ has
○ his

❷ _____ me play, too.

○ Leg
○ Let

❸ Yesterday, he _____ a new puppy.

○ get
○ got

❹ Walk, don't _____ when you cross the street.

○ ran
○ run

Name _____

Read each group of words. Then fill in the bubble next to the word that comes *first* in ABC order.

❶
- ○ draw
- ○ fox
- ○ go

❷
- ○ know
- ○ laugh
- ○ just

❸
- ○ not
- ○ many
- ○ like

❹
- ○ read
- ○ said
- ○ please

Name _____

Read each numbered sentence. Then fill in the bubble next to the correct spelling of the missing word.

1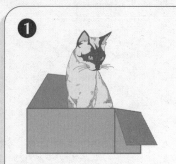

A cat is in ____ box.

○ the
○ they

3

A cat is going ____ a box.

○ into   ○ intow

2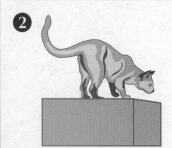

A cat is ____ the box.

○ one
○ on

4

These cats ____ under a box.

○ are
○ ar

Name _____

For each number below, choose the words that would make a complete sentence.

1
- ○ the snow is white
- ○ the snow white
- ○ is the snow

2
- ○ went to school
- ○ she went to school
- ○ she school went

3
- ○ that boy gave me a flower
- ○ a flower that boy
- ○ that boy a flower

4
- ○ the shoe
- ○ on your foot
- ○ put the shoe on your foot

Name _____

Read each numbered sentence. Then fill in the bubble next to the word that is missing in the sentence.

1 **My dad bought a new red ____.**

○ cer
○ car

2 **The cat has lots of ____.**

○ fur
○ far

3 **That girl is nice. I like ____.**

○ her
○ hire

4 **I can tie your shoes ____ you.**

○ for
○ fear

Name _____

For each number below, fill in the bubble next to the word with the *long vowel sound*.

❶

○ boat
○ box

❸

○ fin
○ fine

❷

○ sat
○ state

❹

○ team
○ ten

Name _____

This is a book that Emily checked out from the library.

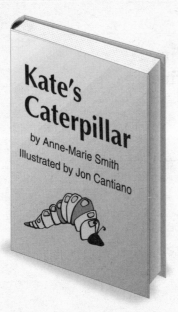

❶ What is the title of this book?

○ Kate's Caterpillar
○ Anne-Marie Smith
○ Jon Cantiano
○ Illustrated by

❷ Who is the author of this book?

○ Kate
○ Anne-Marie Smith
○ Jon Cantiano
○ Emily

Name _____

In each box, look at the picture. On the line write the *two letters* for the first sound in the name of the picture.

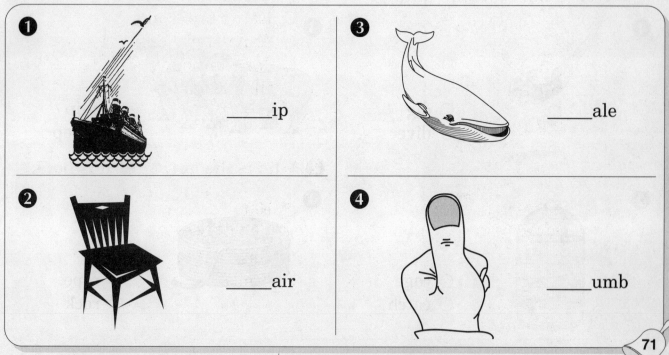

1 _____ip

2 _____air

3 _____ale

4 _____umb

Name _____

For each number below, fill in the bubble next to the word that goes with the picture.

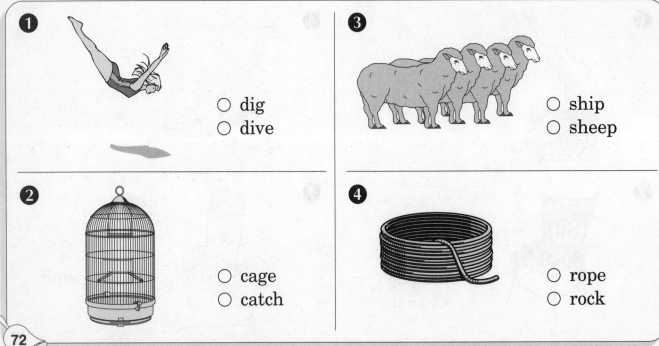

①
○ dig
○ dive

②
○ cage
○ catch

③
○ ship
○ sheep

④
○ rope
○ rock

Name _____

For each number below, fill in the bubble next to the word that goes with the picture.

1
○ rake
○ rack

3
○ goat
○ got

2
○ cut
○ cute

4
○ pain
○ pan

73

Name _____

Read each numbered sentence. Then fill in the bubble next to the correct spelling of the missing word.

1 **Hagop went to _____ house.**

○ hiz
○ has
○ his

2 **I take care of _____ my toys.**

○ all
○ awl
○ al

3 **I _____ read these words.**

○ can
○ kan
○ cane

4 **Haley will ask her mom _____ she can go.**

○ iff
○ if
○ of

Name _____

Read each numbered sentence. Then fill in the bubble next to the correct spelling of the missing word.

1 He _____ my brother.

○ is
○ iz

2 It _____ dark last night.

○ wuz
○ was

3 Come and play a game _____ me.

○ with
○ wiht

4 We can go to _____ house later.

○ hiz
○ his

Name _____

Read the numbered sentence. Then fill in the bubble next to the word that correctly completes the sentence.

① Please _____ me that pencil.

○ give
○ gave
○ gived

② I _____ you walking to school.

○ sees
○ saw
○ seen

③ Yesterday, Raelin _____ to read that book.

○ start
○ started
○ starts

④ _____ the door for me.

○ Open
○ Opens
○ Opened

Name _____

Read each group of words. Then fill in the bubble next to the word that means *more than one*.

❶

○ game
○ games

❷

○ homes
○ home

❸

○ peach
○ peaches

❹

○ day
○ days

Name _____

Read each group of words. Then fill in the bubble next to the word that *does not* belong.

1
- ○ Monday
- ○ April
- ○ Friday
- ○ Saturday

2
- ○ chair
- ○ bed
- ○ book
- ○ table

3
- ○ elephant
- ○ bird
- ○ bear
- ○ tiger

4
- ○ fork
- ○ glass
- ○ cup
- ○ mug

Name _____

Fill in the bubble next to the two words which make up the <u>underlined</u> <u>compound word</u>.

❶ <u>baseball</u>

○ baseb + all
○ base + ball

❷ <u>playground</u>

○ playg + round
○ play + ground

❸ <u>sometime</u>

○ some + time
○ so + metime

❹ <u>birthday</u>

○ birthd + ay
○ birth + day

Name _____

Choose the answer that correctly divides the numbered word into its individual sound segments.

❶ flip

- ○ f/l/ip
- ○ fl/i/p
- ○ f/l/i/p
- ○ fl/ip

❷ stop

- ○ s/t/o/p
- ○ st/o/p
- ○ st/op
- ○ sto/p

❸ swam

- ○ s/w/a/m
- ○ sw/am
- ○ swa/m
- ○ sw/a/m

❹ grand

- ○ gr/an/d
- ○ g/r/an/d
- ○ g/r/a/n/d
- ○ gr/and

Name _____

For each number below, look at the picture. Then fill in the bubble next to the word that means *only one*.

1
○ boy
○ boys

3
○ men
○ man

2
○ buses
○ bus

4
○ pigs
○ pig

Name _____

Read the numbered sentence. Then fill in the bubble next to the word that correctly completes the sentence.

❶ I want to play _____ .

- ○ ball
- ○ bowl
- ○ bill

❸ Get out of my _____ !

- ○ roam
- ○ room
- ○ rime

❷ That's too _____ to go!

- ○ fare
- ○ fair
- ○ far

❹ He is a nice _____ .

- ○ boy
- ○ bay
- ○ bar

Name _____

For each number below, fill in the bubble next to the word with the *long vowel sound*.

1

- ○ pain
- ○ pack

2

- ○ cub
- ○ cube

3

- ○ pitch
- ○ peach

4

- ○ night
- ○ not

Name _____

Read each numbered sentence. Then fill in the bubble next to the word that is missing in the sentence.

❶ The mouse ran _____ of the hole.

○ out
○ art

❷ The lion hurt his _____.

○ pow
○ paw

❸ Jenna found a _____ in the street.

○ count
○ coin

❹ José likes to play with my _____ train.

○ tow
○ toy

Name _____

For each number below, fill in the bubble next to the word with the *long vowel sound*.

❶

○ gate
○ good

❸

○ mule
○ must

❷

○ now
○ nine

❹

○ try
○ tin

Name _____

Read each numbered sentence. Then fill in the bubble next to the correct spelling of the missing word.

1 I ____ to eat my lunch now!

- ○ wahnt
- ○ want
- ○ wunt

2 What ____ you like to eat?

- ○ would
- ○ wud
- ○ woold

3 Come play ____ me.

- ○ wit
- ○ witch
- ○ with

4 I want ____ go home.

- ○ tu
- ○ toe
- ○ to

Name _____

Read each numbered sentence. Then fill in the bubble next to the **correct** spelling of the missing word.

1 **She saw _____ man.**

- ○ the
- ○ they
- ○ thuh

2 **This letter is _____ me.**

- ○ four
- ○ for
- ○ fur

3 **That game _____ fun.**

- ○ wuz
- ○ wos
- ○ was

4 **I like _____.**

- ○ yu
- ○ yo
- ○ you

Name _____

For each number below, fill in the bubble next to the word with the *long vowel sound*.

1

○ mail
○ map

2

○ pine
○ pin

3

○ rock
○ rose

4

○ shell
○ sheep

Name _____

Read each numbered sentence. Then fill in the bubble next to the correct spelling of the missing word.

❶ I _____ two dimes.

○ hafe
○ have
○ hav

❷ I'm glad you _____ my friend.

○ ar
○ air
○ are

❸ Have _____ been here before?

○ they
○ thay
○ thae

❹ My grandma lives far away _____ here.

○ frum
○ frame
○ from

Name _____

Look at the numbered picture. Fill in the bubble next to the word that goes
with the picture.

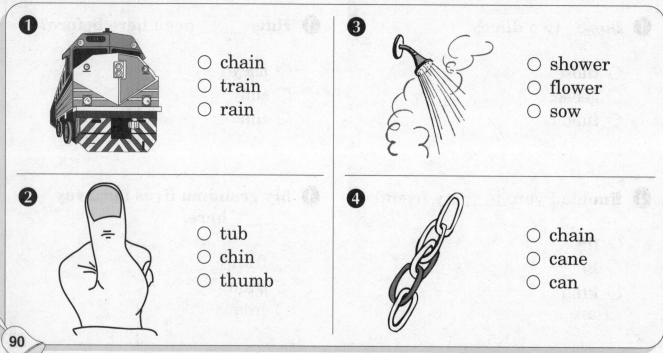

1
- ○ chain
- ○ train
- ○ rain

2
- ○ tub
- ○ chin
- ○ thumb

3
- ○ shower
- ○ flower
- ○ sow

4
- ○ chain
- ○ cane
- ○ can

Name _____

Look at the numbered word. Then fill in the bubble next to the word that has the *same vowel sound* as the <u>underlined letter</u>.

❶ th<u>e</u>se

- ○ those
- ○ geese
- ○ then

❷ f<u>i</u>ne

- ○ fin
- ○ kin
- ○ kind

❸ c<u>u</u>te

- ○ mule
- ○ cut
- ○ cup

❹ b<u>e</u>

- ○ beg
- ○ please
- ○ less

Traci found a book of poetry in the library. This poem was her favorite.

"The Wise Old Owl"

A wise old owl sat in an oak.
The more he heard the less he spoke.
The less he spoke, the more he heard.
Why aren't we like the wise old bird?

- Olivia Raye

1 Who is the author of this poem?

○ The Wise Old Owl
○ Olivia Raye
○ Traci
○ the librarian

2 What is the title of the poem?

○ Book of Poetry
○ Olivia Raye
○ Favorite Owls
○ The Wise Old Owl

Name _____

Read the numbered sentence. Then fill in the bubble next to the word that correctly completes the sentence.

❶ Kate _____ a good day yesterday.

- ○ hid
- ○ had
- ○ hod

❷ Have you _____ your dog today?

- ○ fed
- ○ fid
- ○ fad

❸ He got a new baseball _____.

- ○ met
- ○ mitt
- ○ mutt

❹ Don't _____ my hair too short!

- ○ cot
- ○ cat
- ○ cut

Name _____

In each box, look at the picture. On the line write the *two letters* for the last sound in the name of the picture.

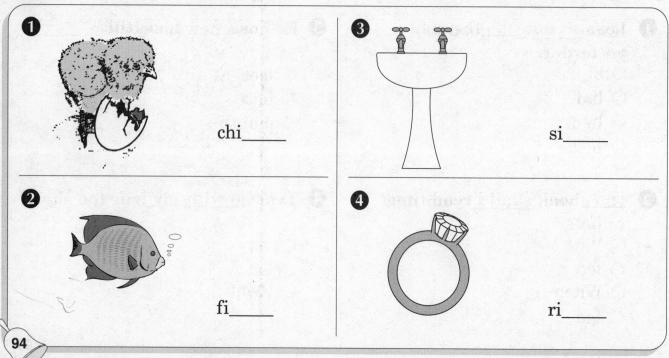

1 chi_____

3 si_____

2 fi_____

4 ri_____

Name _____

Read each numbered sentence. Then fill in the bubble next to the correct spelling of the missing word.

1 Let's sit out ____ the pool.

○ bi
○ bay
○ by

2 ____ book shall I read first?

○ Wich
○ Which
○ Witch

3 Tell me ____ to do this.

○ how
○ haw
○ hoo

4 Let's go with ____.

○ theme
○ the
○ them

Name _____

Read each numbered sentence. Then fill in the bubble next to the word that correctly completes the sentence.

❶ We have two _____.

○ dogs
○ dog

❷ Some _____ cry a lot.

○ baby
○ babies

❸ My dad has many _____.

○ watch
○ watches

❹ All of the _____ are tall.

○ men
○ man

Name _____

For each number below, fill in the bubble next to the words that make an asking or interrogative sentence (a question).

1
- ○ Can you find your book?
- ○ I am reading a book?
- ○ That book has 1,000 pages?

3
- ○ The door open is?
- ○ Did you open the door?
- ○ Open the door?

2
- ○ Zack doesn't know how to dance?
- ○ Dance we shall?
- ○ Shall we dance?

4
- ○ Where is my doll?
- ○ Where my doll is?
- ○ My doll where is?

Name _____

Read the two sentences by each number. Below, fill in the bubble by the word that tells what the sentences are about.

❶ You read it.
It tells stories.

Mom   book   moon
 ○   ○   ○

❷ It looks like a baby.
It is fun to play with.

doll   ball   door
 ○   ○   ○

❸ They go on your feet.
They may be any color.

shirts   snow   shoes
 ○   ○   ○

❹ It lays on the floor.
You sleep on it.

cat   bed   belt
 ○   ○   ○

Name _____

Look at each numbered word. Below it, find the word that has the *same sound* as the <u>underlined letter or letters</u>.

❶ b<u>a</u>ll

   fill   doll   about
    ○   ○   ○

❷ mu<u>ch</u>

  make   cheese   shoe
    ○   ○   ○

❸ st<u>e</u>p

  went   sleep   meat
    ○   ○   ○

❹ w<u>i</u>sh

  went   pin   light
    ○   ○   ○

Name _____

Read the two <u>underlined words</u>. Then choose the correct way to write the contraction for the <u>underlined words</u>.

❶ <u>she is</u>

- ○ she's
- ○ she'll
- ○ she'd

❷ <u>is not</u>

- ○ is'not
- ○ isnt
- ○ isn't

❸ <u>they are</u>

- ○ theyre
- ○ they're
- ○ the're

❹ <u>we will</u>

- ○ we'will
- ○ we'll
- ○ well

Name _____

Read the numbered sentence. Then fill in the bubble next to the word that correctly completes the sentence.

---

1 _____ much is that?

○ Hair
○ How
○ Hew

---

2 You're making _____ much noise.

○ tow
○ toe
○ too

---

3 Don't _____ on the bed!

○ bunch
○ bounce
○ branch

---

4 My pencil has a sharp _____.

○ paint
○ pent
○ point

Read the passage below. Then answer the questions on the next page. You may look back at this page as you answer the questions.

Brad saw a bear at the zoo. The bear was very fat. His coat was brown. He walked slowly on four big <u>paws</u>. He stood up on his back legs, too. It was fun to see the bear.

Name _____

❶ This story is mainly about —

○ coats.
○ legs.
○ a bear.

❷ Who went to the zoo?

○ the zoo
○ four bears
○ Brad

❸ Watching the bear made Brad feel —

○ sad.
○ happy.
○ upset.

❹ The word <u>paws</u> means —

○ step.
○ fat.
○ feet.

Name _____

Fill in the bubble next to the word that rhymes with the numbered words.

① cash, flash, rash, _____

- ○ gas
- ○ shack
- ○ dish
- ○ dash

② bean, mean, jean, _____

- ○ ream
- ○ team
- ○ peace
- ○ lean

③ toe, blow, show, _____

- ○ rope
- ○ Joe
- ○ boat
- ○ hope

④ bunny, honey, funny, _____

- ○ money
- ○ happy
- ○ picky
- ○ tricky

Name _____

For each number below, choose the words that would make a complete sentence.

1
- ○ I have dress
- ○ I have a blue dress
- ○ have a blue dress

2
- ○ the rabbit is eating grass
- ○ rabbit eating grass
- ○ eating grass is the rabbit

3
- ○ dad has brown car
- ○ my dad a brown car
- ○ my dad has a brown car

4
- ○ like to eat peanut elephants
- ○ elephants like to eat peanuts
- ○ eat elephant peanuts

Name _____

Read each numbered sentence. Fill in the bubble next to the word that correctly completes the sentence.

❶ Three _____ live next door.

○ boy
○ boys

❸ Four yellow _____ bring kids to school.

○ bus
○ buses

❷ I like that _____.

○ girl
○ girls

❹ I have two loose _____.

○ tooths
○ teeth

Name _____

Read the numbered sentence. Then fill in the bubble next to the word that correctly completes the sentence.

❶ Elena _____ to school today.

- ○ came
- ○ cam
- ○ kin

❷ I planted the _____ in the soil.

- ○ said
- ○ seed
- ○ side

❸ You did some _____ work!

- ○ four
- ○ fin
- ○ fine

❹ They gave the dog a good _____.

- ○ here
- ○ home
- ○ hum

Name _____

Read each numbered sentence. Then fill in the bubble next to the correct spelling of the missing word.

1 Did you _____ your homework?

○ doo
○ do
○ dew

2 We go to lunch _____ the bell rings.

○ whan
○ wen
○ when

3 May I go _____ to play?

○ out
○ owt
○ oat

4 My mom _____ I could go.

○ sed
○ sayed
○ said

Name _____

Look at each numbered word. Below it, find the word that has the *same sound* as the <u>underlined letter or letters</u>.

1 <u>fee</u>t

    she   fell   them
    ○   ○   ○

2 wa<u>sh</u>

    wear   was   shine
    ○   ○   ○

3 b<u>oy</u>

    join   bay   try
    ○   ○   ○

4 <u>u</u>se

    funny   run   cute
    ○   ○   ○

109

Read the passage below. Then answer the questions on the next page.
You may look back at this page as you answer the questions.

Last night the wind blew very hard. It blew a bird's nest out of the

tree. This morning, Kai found the nest in the street. There were no

eggs in the nest. Kai wondered what happened to the eggs.

Name _____

❶ When did the wind blow hard?

○ this morning
○ today
○ last night

❸ Where was the nest found?

○ in the wind
○ in the street
○ at school

❷ Who found the nest?

○ the wind
○ a bird
○ Kai

❹ How many eggs were in the nest?

○ zero
○ one
○ two

Name _____

Read the numbered sentence. Then fill in the bubble next to the word that correctly completes the sentence.

❶ He _____ to my house to play.

○ comed
○ come
○ came

❷ She _____ that job well.

○ do
○ did
○ done

❸ I hope somebody _____ my lost book.

○ find
○ finds
○ finded

❹ I _____ a little ball of clay.

○ maked
○ making
○ made

Name _____

Read both sentences. Then choose the sentence that has the correct punctuation mark at the end.

❶
○ Was that a good game?

○ Was that a good game.

❸
○ We have a bird and a horse.

○ We have a bird and a horse?

❷
○ I saw a big black bear?

○ I saw a big black bear.

❹
○ Which of these flowers do you like best.

○ Which of these flowers do you like best?

113

Name _____

Mrs. Luong read this poem to her class.

"Laughs"
Troy Barnett

A laugh is just like sunshine.
It brightens every day.
It clears the skies and brings in light,
And drives the clouds away.

A laugh is just like music
With notes upon a sheet,
And melodies with lovely tunes
For making life so sweet.

❶ What is the title of this poem?

○ A laugh is just like music
○ Troy Barnett
○ Laughs
○ For making life so sweet

❷ Who is the author of this poem?

○ Mrs. Luong
○ Troy Barnett
○ The sunshine and the clouds
○ unknown

Name _____

Look at the numbered picture. Fill in the bubble next to the word that goes with the picture.

1
- ○ these
- ○ cheese
- ○ she's

3
- ○ cheap
- ○ sheep
- ○ seep

2
- ○ three
- ○ tree
- ○ tee

4
- ○ wait
- ○ shall
- ○ whale

Name _____

For each number below, look at the picture. Then fill in the bubble next to the word that means *more than one*.

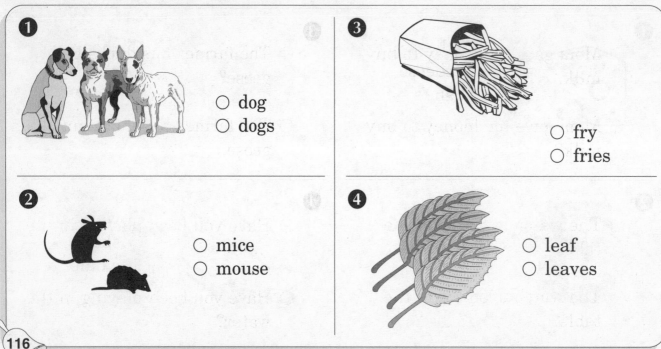

1
- ○ dog
- ○ dogs

2
- ○ mice
- ○ mouse

3
- ○ fry
- ○ fries

4
- ○ leaf
- ○ leaves

Name _____

Read both sentences. Then choose the sentence that has the correct
punctuation mark at the end.

1

○ Mom gave me money to buy
milk.

○ Mom gave me money to buy
milk?

2

○ The watch is on top of the
table.

○ The watch is on top of the
table?

3

○ The farmer has ducks and
geese?

○ The farmer has ducks and
geese.

4

○ Have you been playing in the
water.

○ Have you been playing in the
water?

Name _____

Read the numbered sentence. In the sentence below it, fill in the bubble under the letter that makes a new word and correctly completes the sentence.

❶ I got an apple in my lunch.

What did you g__t?

u   e   a
○   ○   ○

❷ My cat is nice.

Did you c__t your finger?

o   u   a
○   ○   ○

❸ My bed is soft.

How b__d is your pain?

i   u   a
○   ○   ○

❹ Our car was stuck in the mud.

We use glue to make things st__ck.

a   i   o
○   ○   ○

118

Name _____

Read the passage below. Then number the sentences in the order that they happened.

1

When Ming came home from school, he did his homework before he went out to play.

____ He went out to play.

____ Ming came home from school.

____ He did his homework.

Read the passage below. Then answer the questions on the next page.
You may look back at this page as you answer the questions.

Before we eat, Mom calls Anoush. She says,

" Anoush, come and help me. You can set the table."

Anoush puts a plate, knife, fork, and spoon at each place.

After we eat, Lucine helps, too. She takes the dishes to the sink.

Name _____

❶ This story is mainly about —

○ Lucine.
○ the sink.
○ helping.

❸ What happens last?

○ They eat.
○ Lucine takes the dishes to the sink.
○ Anoush sets the table.

❷ In this story, what happens first?

○ Lucine takes the dishes to the sink.
○ Mom calls Anoush.
○ Anoush sets the table.

❹ How many things does Anoush put at each place?

○ two
○ three
○ four

121

Name _____

1 **To write a story, you need to do these three things. Number them in the correct order.**

_____ Put the words on paper.

_____ Think about what you will write.

_____ Edit the story to make it better.

2 **The question above helps you —**

○ tell a story.
○ remember how to write a story.

Name _____

Read each sentence. Then choose the correct spelling of the missing word.

❶ I have _____ feet.

- ○ to
- ○ too
- ○ two

❸ I can _____ well.

- ○ write
- ○ rite
- ○ right

❷ The dolls are over _____.

- ○ their
- ○ there

❹ The toy boat is over _____.

- ○ hear
- ○ here

Read the passage below. Then answer the questions on the next page. You may look back at this page as you answer the questions.

It was May, and I was sitting on our front doorstep trying to eat my chocolate ice-cream cone before the sun could melt it. With each lick, my lips got more and more brown. It was yummy. The chocolate was so sweet and the cone was so crunchy. It was <u>scrumptious</u>! I seemed to be licking everywhere; my hands, my wrists, my lips, and the cone. But, it was worth every lick!

Name _____

❶ This story is mainly about —

○ summer.
○ ice cream.
○ chocolate.

❷ Which of the following words from the passage is a compound word?

○ sitting
○ everywhere
○ doorstep
○ everywhere and doorstep

❸ From the passage, you can tell that <u>scrumptious</u> means —

○ tasty.
○ funny.
○ ugly.
○ dirty.

❹ What was making the ice cream melt quickly?

○ the weather
○ the cone
○ the doorstep
○ the lips

125

Name _____

Read each group of words. Then fill in the bubble next to the word that comes *first* in ABC order.

❶
- ○ upon
- ○ very
- ○ while

❸
- ○ walk
- ○ zoo
- ○ yell

❷
- ○ raise
- ○ pull
- ○ quit

❹
- ○ sing
- ○ table
- ○ ran

Name _____

For each number below, fill in the bubble under the compound word.

❶

fireplace	great	please
○	○	○

❸

shall	both	somebody
○	○	○

❷

small	sailboat	better
○	○	○

❹

sailing	bedroom	many
○	○	○

Name _____

Listen to the sentence. Then fill in the bubble next to the missing word.

1 Dad said, "Come _____ I call you."

○ went
○ when

3 _____ book is on the shelf.

○ His
○ Hit

2 I _____ something to eat.

○ went
○ want

4 I _____ new shoes.

○ gave
○ have

Name _____

(Teacher: Read the directions AND target word.) As I read the word for each number, choose the correct spelling for the word.

1 ○ bird   ○ burd

2 ○ bocks   ○ box

3 ○ fet   ○ feet

4 ○ coat   ○ koat

5 ○ day   ○ dai

6 ○ game   ○ gam

7 ○ rane   ○ rain

8 ○ snow   ○ sno

129

Read the passage below. Then answer the questions on the next page. You may look back at this page as you answer the questions.

Do you like to play in water? Playing in water can be fun. Pedro goes to the beach and jumps in the waves. Nghia swims in a pool at his home.

It is fun to play with toys in the bathtub. Maybe you play with a rubber duck when you take a bath. Lots of kids like to play in water.

Name _____

1 **This passage is mainly about —**

○ playing in waves.
○ playing in water.
○ playing with toys.

3 **Nghia's pool is —**

○ at his home.
○ at the toy store.
○ at the beach.

2 **In this story, Nghia swims —**

○ at the beach.
○ in the bathtub.
○ in a pool.

4 **In the bathtub, you could play with —**

○ a coloring book.
○ a rubber duck.
○ a real elephant.

Name _____

Look at the numbered word. Below it, find the word that has the *same sound* as the <u>underlined letter or letters</u>.

❶ c<u>a</u>me

sad   can   rain
 ◯   ◯   ◯

❷ t<u>a</u>ke

many   saw   eight
 ◯   ◯   ◯

❸ b<u>ir</u>d

party   fur   here
 ◯   ◯   ◯

❹ d<u>ow</u>n

fine   saw   out
 ◯   ◯   ◯

Name _____

Listen to the sentence. Then fill in the bubble next to the missing word.

❶ **I want to give you _____.**

○ something
○ someone

❷ **I _____ do that problem.**

○ carrot
○ can't

❸ **We _____ baseball at recess.**

○ play
○ playing

❹ **You are _____ good work.**

○ does
○ doing

133

Name _____

Look at the numbered word. Then fill in the bubble next to the word that has the *same vowel sound* as the <u>underlined letter</u>.

❶ p<u>a</u>ge

- ○ pain
- ○ peg
- ○ pig

❷ sh<u>e</u>

- ○ beat
- ○ men
- ○ friend

❸ w<u>i</u>se

- ○ wish
- ○ fight
- ○ which

❹ h<u>o</u>pe

- ○ hop
- ○ boat
- ○ coin

Name _____

Fill in the bubble next to the correct word (possessive pronoun) to complete each sentence.

1 **The pink socks are _____.**

○ her
○ hers

2 **Is that _____ towel or mine?**

○ your
○ yours

3 **Cole has _____ own room.**

○ his
○ their

4 **Did you get _____ homework?**

○ my
○ mine

Name _____

Read each group of words. Fill in the bubble next to the word that means *more than one*.

1

○ boy
○ boys

3

○ man
○ men

2

○ goats
○ goat

4

○ lady
○ ladies

Name _____

Read each sentence. Choose the correct spelling for the missing word.

1 Those two _____ are pretty.

○ cat
○ cates
○ cats

2 They _____ cute.

○ look
○ looks
○ looking

3 They are _____ their milk.

○ drink
○ drinkin
○ drinking

4 Grandpa _____ them to us.

○ showd
○ showed
○ showing

Read the passage below. Then answer the questions on the next page. You may look back at this page as you answer the questions.

"Where is Michelle today?" asked the teacher.

Michelle's friend answered, "Her mother is taking her to the doctor. She felt very hot last night, and her head hurt."

"I hope she feels better soon and can come back to school," said Mrs. James.

The next day Michelle came back to school.

Name _____

① Number the sentences in the order that they happened.

____ Michelle went to the doctor.

____ Michelle came back to school.

____ Michelle felt hot.

② Why wasn't Michelle at school?

○ She feels better.

○ The teacher was sick.

○ Michelle was sick.

③ This story takes place at —

○ Michelle's house.

○ the doctor's office.

○ school.

④ From this story you can tell that —

○ Michelle's mother works for a doctor.

○ The doctor is Dr. James.

○ The teacher is Mrs. James.

139

Name _____

Read each sentence. Then choose the correct way to write the contraction for the underlined word(s).

❶ I **cannot** read that word.

- ○ can't
- ○ cann't
- ○ can'nt

❸ **She will** come again.

- ○ She'will
- ○ She'ill
- ○ She'll

❷ **He is** a nice boy.

- ○ H'es
- ○ He's
- ○ Hees

❹ **They are** my friends.

- ○ The're
- ○ They're
- ○ Theyare

Name _____

Read the numbered sentence. Which word would you add to the sentence to tell more about the <u>underlined word</u>?

❶ Nan heard a _____ noise.

○ gray
○ full
○ loud

❷ His mom baked a _____ pie.

○ quiet
○ slice
○ cherry

❸ In the yard, a _____ flower bloomed.

○ beautiful
○ very
○ many

❹ I saw a _____ lion at the circus.

○ cold
○ balloon
○ big

Name _____

Read each sentence. Then choose the correct spelling for the missing word.

1 I will soon _____ seven years old.

- ○ bee
- ○ be

2 My mom went _____ the PTA meeting last night.

- ○ to
- ○ two
- ○ too

3 Did your mom go, _____?

- ○ to
- ○ two
- ○ too

4 I _____ how to spell.

- ○ know
- ○ no

Name _____

Read each numbered sentence. Below it, choose the word(s) that *means the same* as the <u>underlined contraction</u>.

---

❶ <u>It's</u> a beautiful day!

○ It is   ○ It will

---

❸ <u>I'll</u> tell you a secret.

○ I all   ○ I will

---

❷ He <u>can't</u> play today.

○ can tell   ○ cannot

---

❹ He <u>wasn't</u> at home yesterday.

○ was not   ○ was at

143

Name _____

Read the numbered sentence. In the sentence below it, fill in the bubble under the letter that makes a new word and correctly completes the sentence.

❶ Three and one are <u>four</u>.

Matches can start a f__re.

   u   a   i
   ○   ○   ○

❷ The sailors were in the <u>boat</u>.

We need a ball and b__t.

   ai   a   ea
   ○   ○   ○

❸ This food tastes <u>bad</u>.

It is night. It is time for b__d.

   e   u   i
   ○   ○   ○

❹ Turn on the <u>fan</u> to cool the room.

We had f__n at the park.

   u   i   oo
   ○   ○   ○

Name _____

Read each set of sentences. Then fill in the bubble next to the sentence that is written correctly.

❶
- ○ There is a full moon.
- ○ There is a moon full.
- ○ There a moon full is.

❷
- ○ Melody gived me a dime.
- ○ Melody gave me a dime.
- ○ Melody me a dime gave.

❸
- ○ The car didn't start.
- ○ The car didn't start,
- ○ The car start didn't?

❹
- ○ He has a big dog?
- ○ He has a big dog,
- ○ He has a big dog.

145

Read the passage below. Then answer the questions on the next page.
You may look back at this page as you answer the questions.

Bob has a big sister. She is in high school. When
Bob's mom and dad go out, Bob's sister stays at home
with Bob. She reads to Bob and plays games with him.
Sometimes they draw funny pictures. Bob likes to
have his big sister babysit him.

Name _____

❶ Bob is —

○ the big sister.
○ the little brother.
○ the dad.

❸ Bob and his sister draw —

○ rabbits.
○ funny pictures.
○ squirrels.

❷ In this story, who reads to Bob?

○ his mom
○ his dad
○ his sister

❹ In this story, Bob's sister is —

○ nice to him.
○ mad at him.
○ mean to him.

147

Name _____

Read both sentences. Then fill in the bubble next to the sentence that is capitalized correctly.

 1

○ Travis is a boy, and i am a girl.

○ Travis is a boy, and I am a girl.

 2

○ Dad and addison got up early this morning.

○ Dad and Addison got up early this morning.

 3

○ Take this letter to that man over there.

○ take this letter to that man over there.

 4

○ Last night, Sophia came to my house.

○ Last night, sophia came to my house.

Name _____

Read each numbered word. Below it, choose the word that *means the same or almost the same* (synonym) as the numbered word.

❶ big

- ○ small
- ○ large
- ○ little

❷ went

- ○ left
- ○ will
- ○ came

❸ want

- ○ wish
- ○ was
- ○ your

❹ shout

- ○ speak
- ○ short
- ○ yell

Name _____

Read the numbered sentence. Then fill in the bubble next to the word that correctly completes the sentence.

1 **My friends _____ to the movies.**

○ go
○ goes

2 **I hope she _____ me.**

○ choose
○ chooses

3 **Mom _____ to me.**

○ reading
○ reads

4 **My big brothers _____ baseball.**

○ play
○ plays

Name _____

For each number below, fill in the bubble next to the *misspelled* word.

①
- ○ top
- ○ dresss
- ○ hurt

②
- ○ do
- ○ old
- ○ goe

③
- ○ yellow
- ○ litle
- ○ funny

④
- ○ jumpd
- ○ these
- ○ upon

151

During silent reading time in class, Billy read this book.

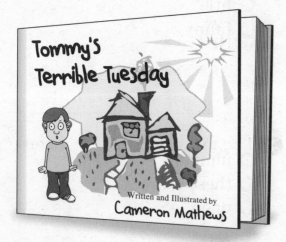

❶ Who is the author of this book?

- ○ Billy
- ○ Tommy
- ○ Billy Mathews
- ○ Cameron Mathews

❷ What is the title of this book?

- ○ Cameron Mathews
- ○ Tommy's Terrible Tuesday
- ○ written and illustrated
- ○ Terrible Tuesday

Name _____

Fill in the bubble next to the correct word (possessive pronoun) to complete each sentence.

❶ That book is _____.

○ my
○ mine

❷ This is _____ sweater.

○ her
○ hers

❸ _____ is the blue bike.

○ His
○ Her

❹ The girls lost _____ shoes.

○ their
○ theirs

Name _____

Read both sentences. Then fill in the bubble next to the sentence that is capitalized correctly.

1

○ When my kitty meows, I pet her.

○ When my kitty meows, i pet her.

2

○ your baby sister is cute.

○ Your baby sister is cute.

3

○ Yesterday, i saw a squirrel.

○ Yesterday, I saw a squirrel.

4

○ That table is too big.

○ that table is too big.

Name _____

Look at the numbered word. Below it, find the word that has the *same sound* as the <u>underlined letter or letters</u>.

❶ <u>wh</u>at

that   hat   which
 ○   ○   ○

❷ <u>sm</u>all

smell   tall   tail
 ○   ○   ○

❸ und<u>er</u>

were   where   went
 ○   ○   ○

❹ h<u>a</u>d

ate   after   make
 ○   ○   ○

155

Read the passage below. Then answer the questions on the next page.
You may look back at this page as you answer the questions.

It is said that seeing a robin is the first sign of

spring. The robin is a brown bird with a red

breast. Many people who have cold snowy winters

look for the first robin. When they see a robin,

they know it will soon be warm <u>outdoors</u>.

1 This story mainly tells about —

○ a bird.
○ snow.
○ winter.

3 If you see a robin in winter, days will probably —

○ get warmer.
○ get colder.
○ freeze.

2 To see a robin means —

○ it is snowing.
○ a bird is singing.
○ it will soon be spring.

4 <u>Outdoors</u> means —

○ inside.
○ outside.
○ beside the doors.

157

Name _____

Think about the parts of a book. Fill in the bubble next to the answer that correctly completes each numbered sentence.

❶ To find out the name of a book, look at —

○ the back cover.
○ the front cover.

❷ To find out the page number a story begins on, look at —

○ the table of contents.
○ the front cover.

❸ To find out what stories are in the book, look at —

○ the table of contents.
○ the teacher.

❹ To find out the name of the author, look at —

○ the cover.
○ the table of contents.

Name _____

Read each numbered word. Below it, choose the word that *means the same or almost the same* (synonym) as the numbered word.

① gone

○ away
○ here
○ later

② choose

○ chop
○ pick
○ carry

③ jump

○ just
○ leap
○ limb

④ start

○ begin
○ star
○ end

Name _____

Read both sentences. Choose the sentence that is written correctly. Look for capital letters and punctuation marks.

1
- ○ Did you hear me.
- ○ Did you hear me?

2
- ○ May I go with you?
- ○ May i go with you?

3
- ○ Ouch, that pan is hot?
- ○ Ouch, that pan is hot!

4
- ○ She lives in Dallas, Texas.
- ○ She lives in dallas, Texas.

Name _____

Read both sentences. Then fill in the bubble next to the sentence that is capitalized correctly.

1
- ○ Today is Monday.
- ○ Today is monday.

2
- ○ Mother's Day is in may.
- ○ Mother's Day is in May.

3
- ○ i can't wait until the weekend!
- ○ I can't wait until the weekend!

4
- ○ The Pilgrims ate corn for Thanksgiving.
- ○ The Pilgrims ate corn for thanksgiving.

Name _____

Choose the answer that correctly divides the numbered word into its individual sound segments.

1 fish

○ f/i/sh
○ f/i/s/h
○ fi/sh
○ fi/s/h

2 cart

○ c/a/r/t
○ ca/rt
○ car/t
○ c/ar/t

3 thin

○ t/h/i/n
○ t/h/in
○ th/i/n
○ th/in

4 chick

○ ch/i/ck
○ c/hi/ck
○ ch/ick
○ c/h/i/c/k

Name _____

For each number below, fill in the bubble next to the words that make a telling sentence (declarative).

1
- ○ I want to be an astronaut when I get older.
- ○ Do you believe there are aliens.
- ○ How do rockets move so fast.

2
- ○ Can a frog really turn into a prince.
- ○ What do you feed frogs.
- ○ Nate has a pet frog.

3
- ○ Do you have a favorite flower.
- ○ My mom's favorite flowers are tulips.
- ○ What kind of flowers are these.

4
- ○ Did Chris score a goal.
- ○ Sarah doesn't know how to play soccer.
- ○ Can we borrow a ball to play with.

Read the passage below. Then answer the questions on the next page.
You may look back at this page as you answer the questions.

Have you read any books by Dr. Seuss? The Cat in the Hat is one of his best known books. Dr. Seuss drew the pictures and made up all of the stories in his books.

Look for books by Dr. Seuss. They are easy and fun to read.

Name _____

1 **Which answer is one word?**

○ the cat in the hat
○ cat
○ the cat is on the hat

3 **Who wrote the Dr. Seuss books?**

○ The Cat
○ The Hat
○ Dr. Seuss

2 **Which words would make a sentence?**

○ the cat in the hat
○ cat
○ the cat is on the hat

4 **Which two words rhyme?**

○ cat, hat
○ easy, fun
○ first, book

Name _____

For each number below, fill in the bubble under the compound word.

1

after   airplane   please

○   ○   ○

2

homework   works   coming

○   ○   ○

3

draw   home   doghouse

○   ○   ○

4

mother   grandmother   her

○   ○   ○

Name _____

Teacher: "I will read the directions and all the sentences. Choose the *best* answer to correctly complete each numbered sentence."

❶ To read the word <u>birthday</u>, —

○ look for two words in the underlined word.

○ ask the principal.

---

❷ In the word <u>rain</u>ing, <u>rain</u> is —

○ the base/root of the word.

○ the ending.

❸ To read the word <u>games</u>, —

○ look for its base/root word and an ending.

○ look in a newspaper.

---

❹ In the word dark<u>er</u>, <u>-er</u> is —

○ the base/root of the word.

○ the ending.

167

Name _____

Look at the numbered word. Below it, find the word that has the *same sound* as the <u>underlined letter</u>.

1 c<u>a</u>ke

can   name   had
○   ○   ○

2 h<u>o</u>me

coat   look   put
○   ○   ○

3 thi<u>s</u>

what   with   ten
○   ○   ○

4 f<u>i</u>nd

one   said   my
○   ○   ○

Name _____

Read the numbered sentence. Then choose the two words that *mean the same* as the underlined contraction.

① **I'm** not going with you.

○ I am   ○ I not

② **He's** a good boy.

○ He is   ○ He had

③ **We're** having fun!

○ We have   ○ We are

④ **She'll** be here soon.

○ She will   ○ She did

Name _____

Read each numbered sentence. Then fill in the bubble next to the correct spelling of the missing word.

1 Those men _____ on TV.

○ wer
○ were
○ where

2 I went to _____ house yesterday.

○ their
○ thaer
○ ther

3 We _____ eat lunch soon.

○ wil
○ will
○ while

4 I can't run _____ fast with a hurt leg.

○ az
○ es
○ as

Name _____

Read each group of words. Then fill in the bubble next to the word that comes *first* in ABC order.

❶
- ○ a
- ○ about
- ○ after

❸
- ○ sleep
- ○ small
- ○ sell

❷
- ○ nut
- ○ not
- ○ night

❹
- ○ me
- ○ may
- ○ my

Name _____

Read the numbered sentence. Which word (adjective) would you add to the sentence to tell more about the underlined word?

1 **Lucas got some** _____ **shoes.**

○ ring
○ new
○ sad

3 **Jacob saw a** _____ **squirrel.**

○ around
○ little
○ well

2 **I have a** _____ **cat.**

○ food
○ play
○ furry

4 **That** _____ **soup tastes good!**

○ bright
○ hot
○ ugly

Name _____

Read each group of words. Then fill in the bubble next to the word that comes *first* in ABC order.

1
- ○ use
- ○ is
- ○ as

2
- ○ start
- ○ shop
- ○ slip

3
- ○ man
- ○ much
- ○ mine

4
- ○ well
- ○ wore
- ○ while

Read the passage below. Then answer the questions on the next page. You may look back at this page as you answer the questions.

Veronika had some food in her hand for the fish. As she leaned over the fish bowl, the fish swam to the top of the water and jumped out. He flew right up into Veronika's hand. Soon all the fish food was gone.

"Thank you," said the fish.

"You're welcome," said Veronika.

The fish flew around the room and then, plop, back into the bowl.

Name _____

① How do you think Veronika felt when the fish flew into her hand?

○ sad
○ surprised
○ mad

② What happened to the fish food?

○ It fell in the bowl.
○ It dropped on the floor.
○ The fish ate it.

③ In this story, the author is trying to —

○ tell a make-believe story.
○ sell fish food.
○ teach you about fish.

④ Could this story really happen?

○ yes
○ no

Name _____

For each number below, fill in the bubble next to the words that make an exclamatory sentence.

1 ○ The blue whale is the biggest whale!

○ Have you ever seen a whale!

○ That whale is huge!

2 ○ Rainbows come out after it rains!

○ Seeing that rainbow was amazing!

○ How many colors are there in a rainbow!

3 ○ I can't believe I hit a home run!

○ Did you hit a home run!

○ My brother plays baseball!

4 ○ Watch out for the car!

○ Do you come to school in your car!

○ We have a white car!

Name _____

Fill in the bubble next to the correct word (possessive pronoun) to complete each sentence.

❶ The baby was sucking _____ thumb.

○ hers
○ its

❷ The kittens could not find _____ mother.

○ their
○ theirs

❸ Is the green cup _____ ?

○ your
○ yours

❹ That is a picture of _____ family.

○ our
○ ours

Name _____

Read the passage below. Then fill in the bubble next to the sentence that tells what happened in the *beginning* of the story.

1

Going to School

Ramses and André are twin brothers. In the morning, Dad calls them to get out of bed. They wash their faces, brush their teeth, get dressed and eat breakfast. Then they walk to school.

After school the boys walk back home together.

○ The boys walk to school.
○ The boys walk home.
○ Dad calls the boys.

Name _____

Read the passage below. Then fill in the bubble next to the sentence that tells what happened at the *end* of the story.

The Softball

Carlos wanted to play on the softball team. He didn't have a softball. He was happy when he got one for his birthday. After his birthday, Carlos practiced and learned to hit the ball well. In the spring he was asked to join the team.

○ Carlos got a softball for his birthday.

○ He joined a team.

○ Carlos learned to hit the ball.

179

Name _____

Read the passage below. Then fill in the bubble next to the sentence that tells what happened in the *middle* of the story.

 Time for Dinner

It was six o'clock in the evening. Mom called Elsa to come in the house and eat dinner. Elsa sat down to eat. She ate lots of meat and potatoes and salad. Then she ate some cookies, too. Elsa left the table when she was full.

○ Mom called Elsa to eat.
○ Elsa ate a lot of food.
○ Elsa was full.

Name _____

Study this table of contents. Then fill in the bubble next to the answer that correctly completes each numbered sentence.

TABLE OF CONTENTS

❶ If you want to read about people who help put out fires, you should start reading on page —

○ 1.   ○ 3.   ○ 5.

❷ This book tells about —

○ jokes.   ○ jobs.   ○ jumping.

Name _____

For each number below, choose the words that make a complete sentence.

1

- ○ Ella reading in the library.
- ○ Ella read the library.
- ○ Ella is reading in the library.

3

- ○ The berries are ripe.
- ○ The berries ripe.
- ○ Ripe the berries are.

2

- ○ The letter in the mailbox I put.
- ○ The mailbox I put the letter.
- ○ I put the letter in the mailbox.

4

- ○ Jack and Jill went up the hill.
- ○ Went up the hill Jack and Jill.
- ○ Up the hill Jack and Jill.

Name _____

Read each sentence. Then choose the sentence that has the correct punctuation mark at the end.

1
- ○ Did you bring your lunch.
- ○ Did you bring your lunch!
- ○ Did you bring your lunch?

2
- ○ That movie was really scary.
- ○ That movie was really scary!
- ○ That movie was really scary?

3
- ○ That's the biggest bird I've ever seen.
- ○ That's the biggest bird I've ever seen!
- ○ That's the biggest bird I've ever seen?

4
- ○ My grandparents live in a tan house.
- ○ My grandparents live in a tan house!
- ○ My grandparents live in a tan house?

183

Read the passage below. Then answer the questions on the next page. You may look back at this page as you answer the questions.

The Bike

Johnny left his bike by the front door. Later he went to put his bike away. The bike had been stolen. He needs his bike to ride to school. Mom says he can ride the bus to school.

Name _____

1 **Who was the story mainly about?**

○ Mom
○ Johnny

2 **What was the problem?**

○ The bike was broken.
○ The bike was stolen.
○ The bike was old.

3 **What can he do now?**

○ His mom can give him a ride.
○ He can walk to school.
○ He can ride the bus.

4 **Which sentence best tells about the whole story?**

○ Johnny walks to school.
○ Johnny's bike was stolen so he will ride the bus.
○ Johnny likes to walk to school.

Name _____

Read the two sentences in each box. Then fill in the bubble next to the best way to put the two sentences together into one sentence.

❶
> **Marie wore a dress.**
> **It was pretty.**

○ Marie wore a dress.
○ Marie wore a pretty dress.

❷
> **Today we had hot dogs.**
> **We had hot dogs for lunch.**

○ We had hot dogs.
○ Today we had hot dogs
   for lunch.

❸
> **She walks to school.**
> **She walks six blocks.**

○ She walks six blocks
   to school.
○ Six blocks to school.

❹
> **Joy has a picture.**
> **It is a picture of a cat.**

○ Joy has a cat.
○ Joy has a picture
   of a cat.

Name _____

Read the passage below. Then choose the best sentence to add to the passage.

1   Tommy is learning to read and to write his A, B, C's. He is learning the sounds of the letters, too.

○ Tommy has dark hair.
○ Tommy is in first grade.
○ Tommy's mother is named Mary.

Name _____

Read each group of words. Then fill in the bubble next to the word that *does not* belong with the other words.

1
○ quick
○ slow
○ stand
○ fast

2
○ knife
○ fork
○ cup
○ spoon

3
○ bedroom
○ street
○ kitchen
○ bathroom

4
○ pen
○ rose
○ pencil
○ chalk

Name _____

Read the numbered sentence. In the sentence below it, fill in the bubble under the letter that makes a new word and correctly completes the sentence.

❶ What <u>time</u> is it?

That animal is t__me.

  a   u   e
  ○   ○   ○

❷ The <u>ship</u> is on the sea.

We will sh__p for a new coat.

  o   e   a
  ○   ○   ○

❸ The soup is too <u>hot</u>!

Wear a h__t in the sun.

  u   i   a
  ○   ○   ○

❹ Walk quietly down the hall.

Their car went down the road.

  u
  ○

Name _____

Fill in the bubble next to the sentence that tells what will happen next.

❶ Margarita's family went out to eat. Margarita wants a hot dog.

○ Margarita will go to the car.
○ Margarita will eat a hot dog.

❷ Lissette's mom took her to the pool. Lissette wants to swim.

○ Lissette reads a book.
○ Lissette goes swimming.

❸ Angelique just got a new baby doll. She loves her new doll.

○ Angelique will play with her doll.
○ Angelique will play a board game.

❹ Antoinette plants a seed in the garden. She waters it and feeds it.

○ The cat will grow.
○ A flower will grow.

Name _____

Read the numbered sentence. Then fill in the bubble next to the word that correctly completes the sentence.

❶ The hot dogs _____ good.

○ smell
○ smells

❸ What do you _____?

○ like
○ likes

❷ I _____ hot dogs at home, too.

○ eat
○ eats

❹ I hope lunch _____ good!

○ taste
○ tastes

Name _____

For each number below, look at the picture. Then fill in the bubble next to the word that means *more than one*.

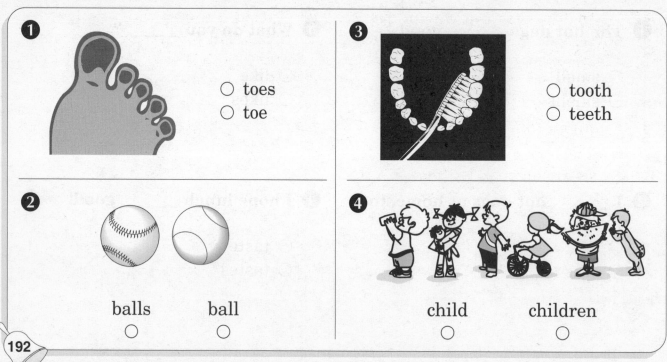

1

- ○ toes
- ○ toe

3

- ○ tooth
- ○ teeth

2

balls   ball
○   ○

4

child   children
○   ○

Name _____

Read each passage. Choose the sentence that does *not* belong.

❶ **Joshua was too warm. He turned on the heater. He took off his coat.**

○ Joshua was too warm.

○ He turned on the heater.

○ He took off his coat.

❷ **Dad planted some fruit trees. He planted apple trees and peach trees. We will have lots of meat.**

○ Dad planted some fruit trees.

○ He planted apple trees and peach trees.

○ We will have lots of meat.

Read the passage below. Then answer the questions on the next page. You may look back at this page as you answer the questions.

"Andy, can you come to my birthday party?" asked Jim.

Andy's mother said he could go.

Andy and his mom went to the store to buy a gift. "Shall I buy a ball, a jump rope, or a book? I like this book. I think I'll give Jim this book," said Andy.

Name _____

❶ Who was the main character?

○ Andy
○ Jim
○ Andy's mom

❸ What was the solution?

○ Andy will buy the ball.
○ Andy will buy the book.
○ Andy will buy the jump rope.

❷ What was the problem?

○ Should Andy go to the store?
○ Should he buy something for Jim?
○ Which gift should he buy?

❹ Why did Andy buy a gift?

○ He didn't like the jump rope.
○ It was for Andy's mom.
○ It was for Jim's birthday party.

Name _____

Read each group of words. Then fill in the bubble next to the word that *does not* belong with the other words.

1
- ○ mother
- ○ father
- ○ sister
- ○ car

2
- ○ April
- ○ winter

3
- ○ whale
- ○ shark
- ○ fish
- ○ lion

4
- ○ hot dog
- ○ pizza
- ○ milk
- ○ burger

195

Name _____

Teacher: "I will read the directions and all the sentences. Choose the *best* answer to correctly complete each numbered sentence."

❶ To read the word <u>doorbell</u>, look for —

○ the root/base word and an ending.
○ two little words.

❷ In the word <u>farmer</u>, look for the —

○ root/base and an ending.
○ two little words.

❸ In the word <u>boxing</u>, the -ing is —

○ the root/base of the word.
○ the ending.

❹ In the word <u>snowed</u>, the -ed is —

○ the root/base of the word.
○ the ending.

197

Read the passage below. Then answer the questions on the next page.
You may look back at this page as you answer the questions.

We are teaching our new dog to obey.   He is learning to "sit." He

should sit still when we say "stay." When we say "come," he

should get up and come to us. When we say "heel," he must

walk close to us. When our dog does what we tell him to

do, we pat his head and say "good dog." He likes that,

and he wags his tail.

Name _____

1 **This story is mainly about —**

○ teaching a dog.
○ going for a walk.
○ having a good day.

2 **The dog must sit still until —**

○ we say "sit."
○ we say "come."
○ we say "good dog."

3 **When our dog does what we tell him to, —**

○ we say "goodbye."
○ we say "come."
○ we say "good dog."

4 **What does the dog do when we pat his head?**

○ He barks.
○ He wags his tail.
○ He runs away.

Name _____

Read the two sentences by each number. Below, fill in the bubble by the word that tells what the sentences are about.

1 She is a girl.
She is in your family.

   brother   sister   father
    ○   ○   ○

2 They are not grown up.
They are boys and girls.

   chairs   shall   children
    ○   ○   ○

3 It is part of your house.
You walk on it.

   foot   floor   flower
    ○   ○   ○

4 It flies in the sky.
It builds a nest.

   bird   airplane   mouse
    ○   ○   ○

Name _____

Look at each sign below. Fill in the bubble next to the word or words that describe the sign.

❶

- ○ Hotel
- ○ Hospital
- ○ Home Sweet Home
- ○ Hamburger Stand

❸

- ○ No Skateboards
- ○ In-line Skating Only
- ○ Don't Walk
- ○ Handicapped

❷

- ○ No Diving
- ○ No Swimming
- ○ No Fishing
- ○ No Playing

❹

- ○ No Smoking
- ○ Smoking is Allowed
- ○ Watch for Fires
- ○ No Eating

Name _____

1 Which of the following icons should you click to tell your computer to print the page?

○   ○

○   ○

3 Which of the following icons should you click to tell your computer to save the page?

○   ○

○   ○

2 Which of the following icons should you click to tell your computer to underline words?

○ B   ○ <u>U</u>

○ *I*   ○ <u>A</u>

4 Which of the following icons should you click to tell your computer to check the spelling?

○   ○ S

○   ○

❶ **While walking home, Luisa saw this sign. She knew to be careful when walking across the _____.**

- ○ rapid river
- ○ rough road
- ○ railroad crossing
- ○ rocky road

❷ **The first graders at Franklin Elementary threw their trash away when they finished lunch. One of the trash cans had the ♳ symbol on it.**

What does this symbol mean?

- ○ Redo
- ○ Review
- ○ Recycle
- ○ Remove

Read both passages below. Then answer the questions on the next page.
You may look back at this page as you answer the questions.

OUR FIELD TRIP TO THE ZOO
by Ming Loo

My class went on a field trip to the zoo today. We saw monkeys, elephants, snakes, and polar bears. My favorite animal was the hippo. They have big mouths, and they like to swim in the water. I had fun at the zoo.

Austin Zoo

The Austin Zoo is a place where people can go to see many different animals. There are lions, elephants, hippos, birds, snakes, giraffes, and many more. Every animal is kept in a cage similar to its natural habitat. Hundreds of people visit the zoo each day. There are many animals for you to see at the Austin Zoo.

Name _____

❶ Both of these passages are about _____.

○ field trips
○ hippos
○ zoos
○ people

❷ From reading <u>both</u> passages, you can tell that _____.

○ the zoo is far away
○ many people go to the zoo
○ monkeys like bananas

❸ From reading <u>both</u> passages, what do you know about zoos?

○ There are more animals than people.
○ Hippos are large.
○ You can see many animals at the zoo.

❹ What animal is mentioned in <u>both</u> passages?

○ birds
○ polar bears
○ lions
○ hippos

Name _____

1 **Which of the following is true in most fairy tales?**

○ The setting is in a forest.
○ The main character is a boy.
○ Someone gets lost.
○ The main character has a friend that is an animal.

2 **Which of the following is true in all myths?**

○ They only discuss animals.
○ Myths are happy.
○ The characters are imaginary.
○ Myths are always funny.

3 **A fictional story is a story that is _____.**

○ true
○ not true

4 **Which of the following is true about all legends?**

○ They are stories from the past.
○ They are stories about the future.
○ They are about Native Americans.
○ They are written by second graders.